REMEMBERING
With The Heart

Stories by America's Finest

Glenna C. Orr
Illustrated by Marinna Bogatov

Published by:
The Kind Kids Inc.
415 Tennessee Ave
Alexandria, VA 22305

Order additional copies of Remembering With The Heart, Stories by America's Finest
from your local bookstore or order copies from
Glenna Orr's website, www.TheKindKids.org, or by calling
The Kind Kids Inc. at 571-214-0162.

Illustrations by Marinna Y. Bogatov
Edited by Yaroslav V. Bogatov

ISBN 978-0-578-51887-9
Library of Congress Cataloguing - In Publication Data

10 9 8 7 6 5 4 3 2 1

Printed in the United States of America

Dedicated To America's Finest

"Life is Hard But So Very Beautiful."
Abraham Lincoln

President Lincoln's Statue

Armed Forces Retiremeent Home (AFRH)

Table of Contents

"Ellie, is that you?" "Yes Gramms, I finally made it home." "Long day at school today?" "That's an understatement, Gramms. Just when I am beginning to believe that I am caught up with assignments, another one comes my way. Eighth Grade classes have definitely kept me plenty busy."

"Joe should be coming along soon. Your brother has baseball practice today. I have some snacks on the kitchen table for the two of you that might take your mind off homework for the time being." "Thanks, Gramms."

"Gramms, there's something else on my mind." "What's that Elanore?" "It's October now, and I am required to complete a certain amount of community service this school year. I'm not quite sure how I want to earn the volunteer credit hours."

"We'll come up with some ideas during dinner tonight, Ellie. Your grandfather and I just might be able to help you with your community service project."

"Hey Gramms, I am so hungry!" "There are snacks on the kitchen table, Joseph. How was baseball practice this afternoon? "Good, really good." When will Pops be home?"

"Your grandfather will be home from work in a bit, Joseph." "What's up Ellie?" "Gramms and I have been talking about school stuff - mostly about my assignments and the volunteer community service that I have to complete for this Eighth Grade school year."

"During dinner this evening, both you and your sister, myself, and your grandfather are going to discuss some ways to volunteer in our community. But for now, Ellie and Joe, please take Liberty and Valor on a walk while I get dinner ready." "Sure thing, Gramms."

"Joe, how is school going?" "It's okay. Fifth Grade is harder than Fourth Grade, but I'm good with it - so far so good. My baseball team is great. Playing with the same players that I played with in the spring, makes practices and games a lot more fun."

"You doing okay, Ellie?" "I am, Joseph. I know that sometimes I talk a lot about my school assignments, but it's only because I want Gramms and Pops to be a part of it all. Part of it for the both of us."

"We had better head home, Ellie. Pops should be home from work and I, for one, am ready for dinner."

"Hi Elanore and Joseph. And, there's our Liberty and Valor...did you all have a good walk?" "Yes, we did Pops. So, how was your day at work, Pops?"

"Thanks for asking, Joseph. It was a good day; my co-workers and myself began a new project today and we seemed to accomplish a lot. Let's talk more during dinner, because I certainly want to learn all about your day at school. " "Ellie and Joe, please take a few minutes to get ready for dinner." "Will do, Gramms.

"Emma, thank you for preparing such a delicious dinner. I know that we are all grateful for having this meal together." "You are most welcome, John."

"So, who is the first to tell me about their day?" "I'll go first, Pops. Baseball practice was great. Our team plays so well together. My next game is Saturday, at 11:00 am." "And school, Joe...how about school?" "School is fine. Challenging sometimes, but all is okay."
"John, Elanore and I were talking earlier today about the Eighth Grade Community Service project that she wants to begin. Ellie and I thought that you might have some ideas for her volunteer efforts."

"Ellie, what are your thoughts about the project?" "I am not totally sure, Pops. The Community Service Project is meant to provide service to those who need help. And, I believe it would be a good idea to volunteer my time in a place where Joseph might be able to join me from time to time."

"Your Gramms and I will give it some thought, Elanore. We can talk about the project more tomorrow. But for now, let's enjoy our dinner together."

Breakfast Time

"Ellie, your grandmother and I have come up with an idea that may be helpful with your community service project. I am going to speak with a friend of mine today. She is the librarian at The Armed Forces Retirement Home, one of America's oldest veteran's retirement homes. I believe that both yourself and Joe would enjoy volunteering there."

"Thanks, Pops, sounds like a good idea. I am wondering what kind of volunteering we could do at the retirement home." "There will be plenty of ways that you can be of service to the veterans that reside at The Armed Forces Retirement Home, Ellie. Now off to school." "Thanks for breakfast, Gramms."

"Joe, good luck at your game today. I'm sorry to be missing it." "That's okay, Ellie. There will be many other baseball games for you to attend. Gramms will be cheering for my team. And, besides, I think that you and Pops will have a very interesting afternoon.

"Good luck, Joseph, have a great game!" "Thanks, Pops."

"Ellie, please meet my friend and colleague, Christine Baldwin who is the librarian of The Armed Forces Retirement Home." "Good to meet you Ellie, and welcome. Your grandfather tells me that you are wanting to earn service hours for an Eighth-Grade community service project." Yes, Ms. Baldwin, that's right."

"Well, Ellie, some of our residents who reside here at The Armed Forces Retirement Home often times could use help with their daily activities, or perhaps would enjoy your reading to them. Our veterans here at the Home have led such interesting lives and I believe that you will learn a great deal from them." "Ms. Baldwin, would it be possible for my brother Joe to accompany me and volunteer as well?" "Certainly, Joe is more than welcome."

"If you would like Ellie, you can begin your volunteering this coming week." "That would be great Ms. Baldwin. Would 3:30 pm on Wednesday be a good time to start?" "Most definitely, Ellie. We'll see you then."

"Hi Ellie, great that you are here today. We are going to take a walk to the Scott Building. I want to introduce you to Mr. Edward Davis, one of our residents here at The Armed Forces Retirement Home. You and I will spend some time listening and speaking with retired First Sergeant Davis. First Sergeant Davis has had quite an interesting military career.

"Ms. Baldwin, what is Mr. Davis like?" "Well, Ellie, he is ninety-five years old. First Sergeant Davis is a Pearl Harbor survivor, and he served in both the Korean War and the Vietnam War. Mr. Davis has a strong love for the United States of America, and for the men who served in combat with him during his military career."

"Mr. Davis, I would like for you to meet Ellie. Ellie will be volunteering at The Armed Forces Retirement Home during this school year." "Hello Ellie." "Hi Mr. Davis, it is good to meet you. Your room is very nice, and I like all of the photographs that you have displayed."

"Well, thank you so much, Ellie. My favorite photographs are of my daughter, Deborah, and of my son, Fred. The remainder of my photos are of my military career."

"We have been studying about World War II in school this year. Were you a soldier in WWII?" "Yes, I was. At the time, I was living in Schofield Barracks, located on the island of Oahu in Hawaii. I had been trained by the United States Army to be a "Signal Wireman.""

My Infantry Unit was called "The Wolfhounds." Our unit and other units as well, worked together to support other soldiers and to protect the many civilians and many members of the United States Military who were living and working at the United States Naval Base, Pearl Harbor, the lagoon harbor on the island of Oahu, Hawaii in what was then the United States Territory of Hawaii.

Pearl Harbor

"On December 7, 1941, at about 8:30am while eating breakfast in the Mess Hall, I heard several explosions. Then I went outside and witnessed low flying aircraft with red circles marking their wings. The Japanese were attacking our U.S. Naval Base at Pearl Harbor. It was a surprise military strike conducted by The Imperial Japanese Navy against the United States. There were nearly simultaneous Japanese attacks on the United States held Philippines, Guam, and Wake Island, and on the British Empire in Malaya, Singapore and Hong Kong."

"What happened next, Mr. Davis?"

"The Wolfhounds," my Infantry Unit, loaded our wire truck with communications equipment, as we were assigned to do. My unit then proceeded to travel to particular sites on the island of Oahu, Hawaii, and put in place a variety of communication equipment. So much of Oahu was engulfed in flames and smoke due to the surprise military strike by the Imperial Japanese Navy. Pearl Harbor was a horrific sight. Ships were in the harbor grouped three side-by-side. Some ships were leaning, some burning, and some of the ships were capsized on their side. At each stop we made, we installed communication equipment. Members of my Infantry Unit, "The Wolfhounds," would then stay at the designated posts to defend that particular place - all for our country. As for myself, after all the necessary equipment was in place in all locations, I settled down near the switchboard in a locker room in Roosevelt High School that overlooked Honolulu and Waikiki Beach."

"I made this place my home for about the next six months. What I learned on December 7, 1941, and the subsequent days that followed have remained with me to this day. Life is truly fragile."

"Mr. Davis, Ellie and I should let you have some time to yourself - the Mess Hall will be serving dinner soon." "Thanks, Christine, for bringing Ellie by for a visit. I am grateful for the company." "Ellie, there is something that I have said many times and have believed my entire life." "What is that Mr. Davis?" "Don't ever give up. Have fortitude and believe in yourself." "Thank you, Mr. Davis for sharing your military career with me. It helps me to understand somewhat better about World War II and the topics that we are learning about in History class."

"Hope to see you again, Ellie. Perhaps you can read to me the next time you come to visit."

"Ms. Baldwin, I see that my grandfather is waiting for me. I'll catch up with him. Thank you so much for introducing me to Mr. Davis. I learned so much from listening to him." "You are most welcome, Ellie. First Sergeant Davis is a very distinguished veteran of our United States of America."

DINNER TIME

"Ellie, tell me something about your volunteering today at The Armed Forces Retirement Home." "Sure, Gramms. Ms. Baldwin, the librarian at the home, introduced me to First Sergeant Davis. He served in the United States Army for thirty years. Mr. Davis is a hero. And, what I learned from talking with him today will truly help me to understand better what I am studying in school this year. Ms. Baldwin and I have set a time for me to return to The Armed Forces Retirement Home in two weeks. Hope that's okay." "Certainly will be, Ellie. I am glad that your time spent with First Sergeant Davis and Ms. Baldwin was enjoyable."

CHAPTER 3
CATHERINE DEITCH, FIRST SERGEANT
WAC - Women's Army Corps, WWII

"Welcome back, Ellie." "Thanks, Ms. Baldwin." "It's Wednesday, and some of our residents will be playing Bingo in the Community Center this afternoon. I would like to introduce you to someone who will be there. We can actually meet up with Catharine Deitch prior to the start of Bingo, and then it might be fun for you to help the residents with Bingo this afternoon." "Good idea, Ms. Baldwin." "Great, Ellie, let's catch up with First Sergeant Catharine Deitch - I believe we can find her."

"Hi Catharine, this is Ellie. She is volunteering at our Home and earning service hours for an Eighth Grade School project." "Hello Ellie, good to meet you. How do you like volunteering at our Home?" "So far, I have been able to visit with First Sergeant Davis, and I have learned a lot about World War II from talking with him." "Great, Ellie. Mr. Davis is a remarkable man that has had an extraordinary military career."

"I, too, served our country during World War II. My active duty date began December 30, 1942. I traveled on a troop train to Daytona Beach, Florida, arriving just as the whistles were blowing to welcome the New Year, 1943. My husband reported for duty on January 10, 1943, so he bid me farewell and followed shortly behind me. I served in the WAAC, the Women's Army Auxiliary Corps, from December 30, 1942 to August 9, 1943, and then served in the WAC, Women's Army Corps, from August 9, 1943 to November 24, 1945."

AT MY DESK

"After Basic Training at Daytona Beach, I was assigned to Boston, Massachusetts, and lived at the Boston City Club for fifteen months. I worked in the orderly room. From Boston, I was sent to Bradley Field, Connecticut and later to Fort Oglethorpe, Georgia."

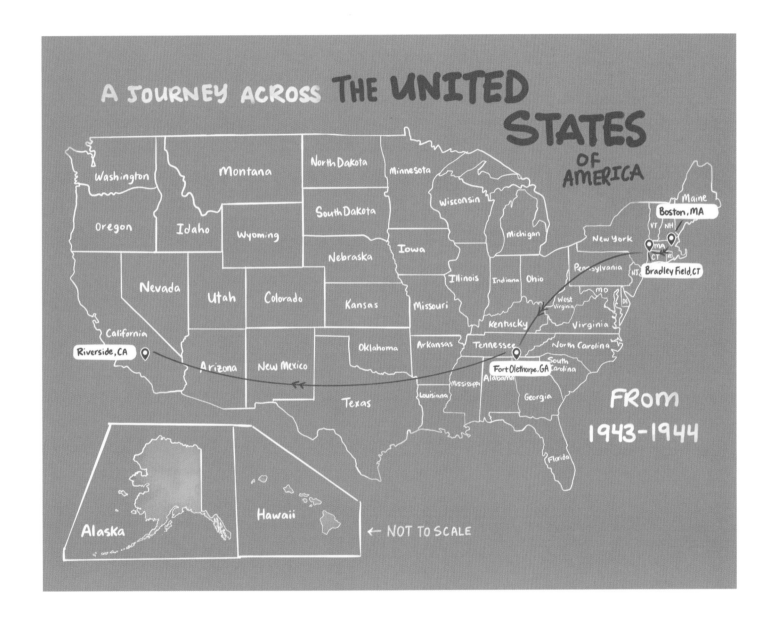

"And, from Georgia I was sent on a troop train to Riverside, California to prepare for an overseas assignment. I still have a copy of the list of 113 women who sailed with me on September 26, 1944 on the USS General A.E. Anderson."

Bombay, India
ARRIVED: October 28, 1944

"Since our ship, the General A.E. Anderson had to "zigzag" while crossing the Pacific Ocean to avoid being sunk by enemy submarines, it meant that we were on board from September 26, 1944 until we arrived at Bombay, India via the Indian Ocean on October 28, 1944. We had made only one stop, and that was in Melbourne, Australia. We stayed in Melbourne for one week to refuel the ship."

"We then flew from Bombay to Calcutta, India, on C-47 airplanes. Upon our arrival to Calcutta, we were driven to Hastings on the Hooghly River, a branch of the Ganges River. There, very close by, we lived in a huge jute mill which the U.S. Army had converted for our living quarters."

"Our jobs were those of clerical workers, telephone operators, trainer specialists, cooks, and medical staffers. While I lived in India, I visited the Taj Mahal, saw Mount Everest, Darjeeling in West Bengal, and other intriguing places."

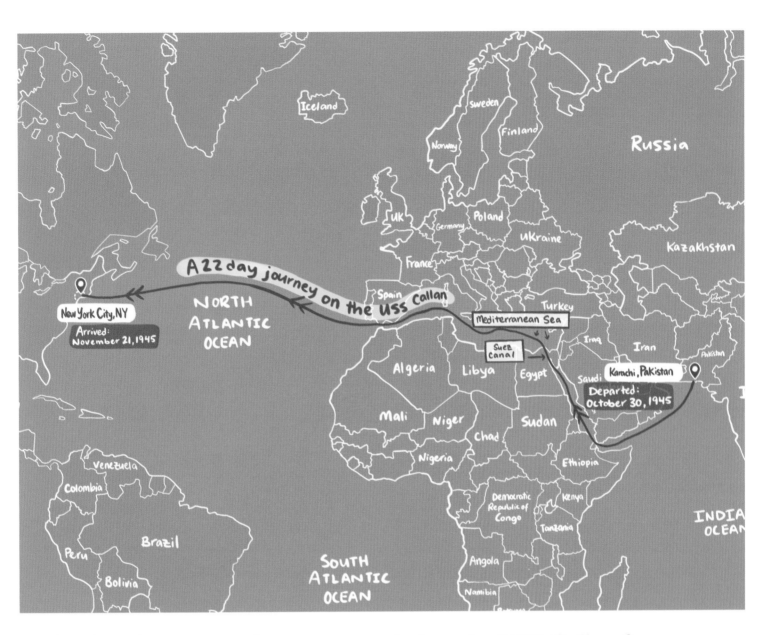

"On October 30, 1945, my group sailed on the USS Callan from Karachi, Pakistan back to the United States, through the Suez Canal, the Mediterranean Sea, the North Atlantic Ocean and arrived in New York City on November 21, 1945."

"I then traveled to Fort Dix, New Jersey and was discharged on November 24, 1945. It was Thanksgiving Day and we were served a feast!" "Ellie, my service in the United States Army afforded me the opportunity to sail all the way around the world. And when people ask me what I did while serving my country, I tell them that I was an Administrative Specialist with duty as a WAC Detachment First Sergeant at Headquarters, Burma Theater, Calcutta, India. I loved my years serving our country - very exciting and all of my extraordinary experiences have made an impact on my life to this very day."

"Mrs. Deitch, maybe you could give me some notes about all of your travels during the years of your military service. It would be interesting to study a map, and track all of your journeys." "Ellie, I can surely do that. The next time that you volunteer at The Armed Forces Home, I will have some notes ready for you." "Thanks so much, Mrs. Deitch." But for now, Ellie, would you like to join me and some of my friends for a game of Bingo?" "Sure, Mrs. Deitch, I would like that."

"Ellie, may I share some of my personal thoughts with you?" "Yes, of course." "It is important to have courage and strength, and to do the best that you can. Always encourage others along the way who are needing help and guidance. Be accepting and do the best that you can for yourself and for others. I have tried to live by my beliefs throughout my entire life. And, as the years pass by, my beliefs have become even stronger. "Thank you, Mrs. Deitch for sharing your thoughts with me.

Would you like for me to help you get into the Community Center?" "Ellie, I thought you would never ask...let's play Bingo!"

"Joseph, I am glad that you could accompany your sister Ellie today. November 11, here, at The Armed Forces Retirement Home, is a very special day." "Thanks, Ms. Baldwin. Ellie has been telling our family about her times here at the retirement home...she likes it here a lot. Do you have the same celebration each year for Veteran's Day?"

"Yes Joseph, we surely do. As you have seen from the opening ceremonies, the reciting of The Pledge of Allegiance to our Flag, and listening to guest speakers, the residents here at The Armed Forces Retirement Home are all veterans who have served their country.

Veteran's Day is an official federal holiday in the United States that commemorates the service of all U.S. military veterans. Veteran's Day was once called Armistice Day. Armistice Day was created to honor veterans of World War I. November 11, 1919 was the first day Armistice Day was celebrated. The country of Germany signed the armistice, ending the hostilities of WWI in the 11th month, on the 11th day, during the 11th hour. On June 1, 1954, the United States government changed the name to Veteran's Day in order to honor all military veterans."

"It sure is something to see - so many people celebrating together and having a good time." "You are so right, Joseph."

"Ms. Baldwin, the man in his wheelchair next to the bench looks like he could use a little help with his food tray. Let's see if we can help him. "Joe, I would like for you to meet Mr. Robert Webb."

"Hi, Mr. Webb. It looks like you could use a little help - mind if I lend you a hand?" "Hello Joe, good to know you. And, you are so right about my needing some help. If you could hold my tray of food while I put my bottle of water in my cup holder on the side of my wheelchair, that would be great." "Sure thing, Mr. Webb." "Now tell me Joseph, what brings you to our Home today?" "My sister Ellie, has been volunteering here at your Home, and I am here with her today." "Welcome, Joseph. We are glad that you have come for our Veteran's Day celebration."

"Mr. Webb, did you grow up in a city like Washington, D.C.?" "Oh no, Joseph. When I was your age, I was living in Ohley, West Virginia. Our family had a farm - we had gardens, and raised hogs and chickens. There were nine children in our family, seven boys and two girls. My mother and father were always doing such kind deeds for people... especially people who never seemed to have enough food to eat. When I got a little bit older, our family moved to East Bank, West Virginia. While in high school, I played football and baseball. Do you play a sport, Joseph?"

"I play baseball, Mr. Webb. My sister Ellie and I live with our grandparents. My Gramms and my Pops hardly ever miss my practices and games. I play third base and I am a pitcher sometimes." "Good job, Joseph. Playing a sport will teach you many worthwhile lessons."

"Mr. Webb, my sister Ellie has been telling me about the military careers of some of the people that she has met here at The Armed Forces Home. I would like to learn about yours." "Have you studied much about World War II, Joseph?" "Our class has studied about this time in history, some. My sister Ellie is in Eighth Grade, and she is learning a lot about what happened during those years."

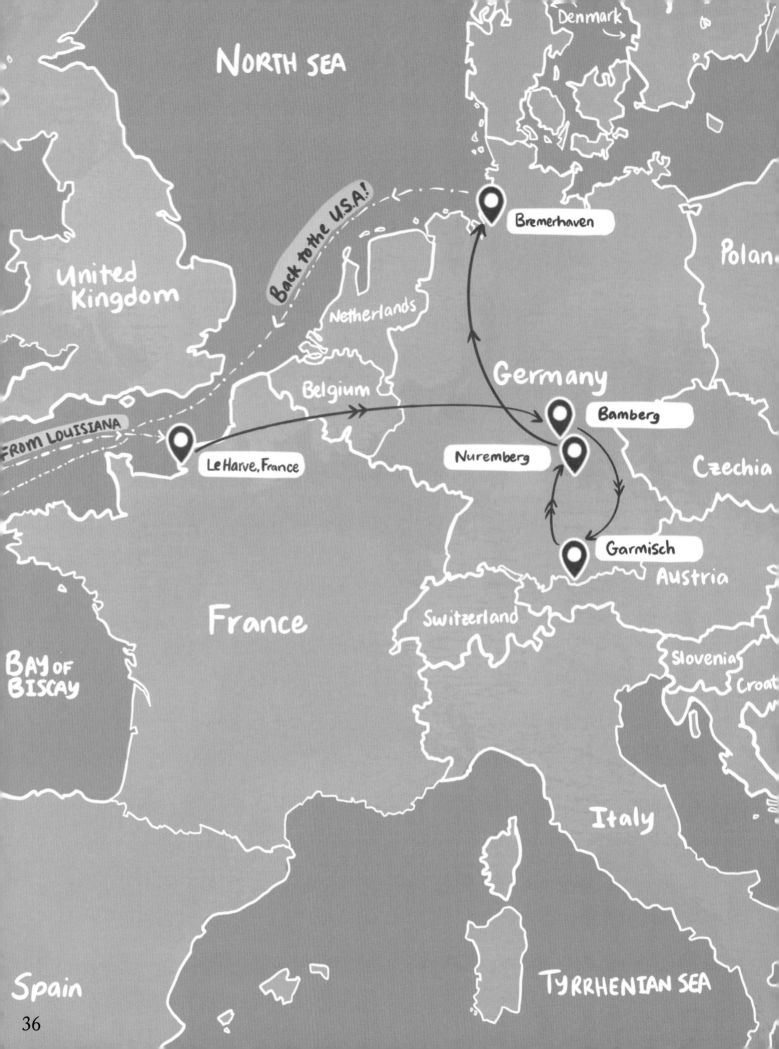

"Two of my brothers joined the United States Army Air Corps, one of my brothers the United States Navy, and another brother joined the United States Marine Corps during World War II. So, I decided to join the United States Army. Every branch of the service was now covered by the Webb Family. After I enlisted in the United States Army, I was sent for basic training to Camp Livingston, Louisiana.

After three short assignments, my unit went on a Merchant Marine ship called the Seacat. My first station was Le Havre, France. At eighteen years of age, I saw the aftermath of war. Then, I moved through France to Bamberg, Germany aboard a boxcar train. It was December and so very cold. So cold that it was hard to sleep. I took some training in Bamberg. "

"Then, I traveled to Garmisch, Germany where I attended Military Ski School for two weeks. However, my toughest assignment was standing guard to the Nazi War Criminals, just outside of Nuremberg, Germany. I also worked guarding the elite guard of the Nazi Party at the SS Trooper Prison Camps along with a company of Polish Soldiers. I then went on to Bremerhaven, Germany and then returned to the United States."

"After the war, I went to college in West Virginia at Morris Harvey College, now known as University of Charleston. It was there that I earned a degree in Engineering. Later, I attended the University of Chicago and graduated with a degree in Structural Engineering. I have had a very rewarding life, Joseph. Remember to set goals for yourself, and when you achieve those goals, then set another goal - even higher. Don't ever give up. Have faith that you will accomplish great things."

"Thank you, Mr. Webb, for sharing your life story with me. So that I remember your story, I will write it all out. Maybe when I can come back for another visit, I can read it to you." "That would be great, Joseph. Thank you for spending time with me this afternoon." "You're welcome, Mr. Webb."

"Good idea that we wore our jackets, Joe. It's cold." "You are right about that Ellie, but Liberty and Valor are surely liking their walk." "Joe, I am going to The Armed Forces Retirement Home on Saturday to volunteer - would you like to go with me?" "I really can't, Ellie. I have too much school stuff to catch up on. If you see Mr. Webb, please tell him hello for me. I learned so much from talking with him."

"Hi Ellie, glad that you could make it today." "Thanks, Ms. Baldwin." "I would appreciate your help in the library today, Ellie. And, I would like for you to meet one of our residents here at The Armed Forces Retirement Home. She helps me quite frequently here in the library. Ellie, meet Mrs. Norma Gene Strawn Rambow." "Hello Ellie, so good to meet you." "Norma, it would be a big help to me, if you and Ellie could shelve some of the books here in the library this afternoon. Ellie has been volunteering with us here at the Home - she is earning hours for an Eighth Grade Community Service project." "Good for you, Ellie. I was an Elementary School Teacher for twenty-seven years and I so enjoyed working with children. I taught First and Second Grades in Battle Creek, Michigan. Let's get to shelving these books Ellie, and if it's okay with you, we can continue our conversation."

"This library is such a special place for our residents here at The Armed Forces Retirement Home. Have you ever seen so many books...there is something here for everyone. Do you like to read, Ellie?" "Yes, I do Mrs. Rambow." "Oh, please Ellie, call me by my first name, Norma." "Norma, how long have you lived here?" "It's been four years now, Ellie. I moved here from Battle Creek, Michigan. I was born in Sullivan County, Indiana and at age thirteen I moved to Terre Haute, Indiana. When I was eighteen years old, I was a freshman at Indiana State Teacher's College in Terre Haute. The year was 1941. A terrible thing happened to our country on December 7, 1941 - Pearl Harbor was bombed by the Japanese."

41

AT THE BARRACKS

"I love our country and wanted to help defend it. On February 13, 1943, the United States Marine Corps Women's Reserve was established and I was finally able to join up. After being sworn into the Marine Corps Women's Reserve, I had to wait a few months and then I was called to active duty on November 15, 1943.

Next, I was off to Boot Camp at Camp Lejeune, North Carolina. It was such an honor for me to be living and working with girls from across this great country. After graduating from Boot Camp on December 24, 1943, I went to Cooks and Baker's School. When I completed this training, I was assigned to Mess Hall 54 Battalion Area at Camp Lejeune. Cooking, grinding coffee, and performing many other duties kept me plenty busy - I was proud when I got my Corporal Stripes.

Then, I went on to serve as an Assistant Cook, a Chief Cook, and a Wing Sergeant - these jobs taught me how to supervise the girls in the Mess Hall. Later on, I became a Supply Sergeant. The friendships during my years as a United States Marine were a blessing."

"Did you stay at Camp Lejeune for a lot of years, Mrs. Rambow - I mean Norma?" "No Ellie. On November 16, 1945 I had enough points for discharge, and was anxious to get out and start the winter term at Indiana State Teacher's College in Terre Haute.

Before I begin to tell you about the next phase of my life experience, let me identify to you some highlights of my military career. One was going home to Indiana twice a year when my big brother was home from the Navy. Plus, I enjoyed several tours in the Washington, D.C. area. I took advantage of three-day passes and enjoyed the Capital City immensely. I never dreamed that I would live here one day. I made friendships with a lot of girls during my Marine days. One was Rose Crowder from Brooklyn, New York. I was a guest in her family's apartment. Rose's sister and I visited the Statue of Liberty and other tourist attractions in the city. When discharged from the Marines I traveled to Norfolk, Virginia to see my stepbrother who was in the Navy."

READY FOR THE HOLIDAYS

43

ON MY SUMMER BREAK

"Next, I journeyed back to my home state of Indiana just in time to start the winter term to complete my sophomore year at Indiana State Teachers' College. I was privileged and very grateful to be able to take advantage of the G.I. Bill to further my college education.

However, my plans changed because at that time my mother now lived in Battle Creek, Michigan. My mother invited me to visit her and her new family in Battle Creek for the summer. I was doing well in college and at age twenty-two, I should have stayed in college to pursue my dream of becoming an elementary school teacher. However, I did take the summer break from college, went to Battle Creek, and found work at a neighborhood drugstore that summer. Working in a neighborhood pharmacy kept me busy. While working there, though, I met a handsome young man and we were married in April of 1947. Our lives were blessed to have a daughter and a son."

44

"In 1956, with the help of my husband and friends, I once again became a college student. Earning a Bachelor of Science Degree and later a Master's Degree in Education was so much work for me and so rewarding. I had the best time being a teacher - for twenty-seven years. I felt I was at home in the classroom. How about yourself, Ellie - what do you like about school?"

"I love to read, Norma, and I write in journals all of the time. I like school. My brother Joseph and I live with our grandparents - we have for the past year. "Ellie, would you like to get a snack with me at our Mess Hall? I believe that we have shelved all of the books." "That would be great, Norma. I'll need to call my grandparents and let them know I'll be staying here at the Home a bit longer."

"Hello, Bill." "Hi Norma, getting the library straightened around, are we?" "Yes, we are, Bill. Our residents certainly do love to read, and the books just come and go from our great library. Bill, I would like for you to meet a volunteer here at The Armed Forces Retirement Home. Ellie, I would like for you to meet Mr. Opferman." "Hi Ellie, good to meet you. Welcome, and thank you very much for volunteering at our Home." "Ellie, Mr. Opferman shows films to our residents every Sunday afternoon. It's quite a job for him, because he prepares announcements that tell the residents about the films that he is showing that particular Sunday."

"What kinds of films do you show, Mr. Opferman?" "Well Ellie, it sometimes depends on the holidays that we are celebrating, and of course, our residents make recommendations. You know Ellie, perhaps you would like to help me with showcasing a movie sometime." "Thank you, Mr. Opferman. I can talk with my grandparents about it, and Ms. Baldwin as well. "Okay Ellie, let's be on our way. I have worked up an appetite from shelving all of the books!"

"Gramms, I think I have time for another visit to The Armed Forces Home before our Winter Break starts." "What do you have in mind, Ellie?" "A resident, Mr. Opferman, shows movies on Sunday afternoons. I could help him pass out flyers to the residents and help him with the popcorn machine." "That should be fine, Ellie. Maybe Joseph could join you." "Thanks, Gramms."

"Hi Ms. Baldwin and Mr. Opferman. Mr. Opferman, this is my brother Joseph. He is volunteering with me today." "Good to meet you Joseph." "Thank you." "Joseph, we are glad that you returned to our Home to help out." "Glad to be here Ms. Baldwin. It sure looks different with all of the Christmas decorations - they are everywhere." "Yes Joseph, it's quite beautiful here at The Armed Forces Retirement Home during the holidays. I do need to return to the library to help the residents. If you need me for anything, you will find me somewhere in the library. I know how much Mr. Opferman appreciates your help today."

"So, Ellie and Joseph, let's get to work. This afternoon we are showing a holiday movie entitled, "Miracle On 34th Street". I have shown this particular movie during Christmas and the residents enjoy watching it very much. Routinely, I prepare programs for the movies - the programs give information about the actors that are featured in the films and about the times being portrayed in the movies. Please take a look at today's program."

"It looks like you have put a lot of effort into this, Mr. Opferman." "Keeps me busy, Joseph and I do enjoy giving my time to enriching the lives of my friends here at The Armed Forces Retirement Home." "How can we help, Mr. Opferman?" "Ellie, it would be helpful for you and Joseph to fold the programs for me. We have about an hour before the residents begin arriving to the Community Center - there's plenty of time."

"Do you like to read, Ellie and Joseph?" "Ellie reads all the time, Mr. Opferman and she writes in her journal a lot." "How about yourself Joseph - do you enjoy reading?" "Yes, I do; however, not nearly as much as my sister does." "My mother loved to read, Mr. Opferman, and she used to watch older movies with her father while she was growing up. I guess that's why even as an adult, watching older films was fun for her. Joseph and I miss her so much. She died three years ago." "I'm sorry to hear this, Ellie."

"Our father has assignments that take him away from the United States. He stayed very close to Joseph and me for these past three years." "Our dad will be coming home for Christmas. Joseph and I are living with our grandparents, my mother's parents." "Gramms and Pops are so good to Joseph and me - we love them very much."

"Mr. Opferman, have you always lived in this area?" "No, Joseph. Our family lived in Pittsburgh, Pennsylvania until I was four years old. Then, we moved to New York City. At the time, there were just two children in our family. One sister, Anne Regina, had died as a baby. But over the years in New York, there were five more, one boy and four girls. Our family stayed in New York City and I grew up there. I became very interested in studying history and geography. I also enjoyed reading literature about Detective Sherlock Holmes - the author was Arthur Conan Doyle, and the Father Brown stories of G. K. Chesterton. From these and many detective-story magazine articles, I learned several investigative techniques that were useful to me later in life. When I was eighteen years old, I joined the United States Army - it was 1948. I was trained to be a radio operator."

AS GEN. WALKER'S GUARD

AT MY BARRACKS

"I did not choose that line of work, but the U.S. Army picked the job for me. The Horse Cavalry is what I really wanted for a job, but it no longer existed.

In 1949, I was sent to Japan as a radio operator in the Signal Corps, in Yokohama. Then I was assigned as a transmitter attendant in Kawasaki. This was a responsible position and it made me feel very proud. However, I preferred guard duty as a full-time career-type job. While still in Japan, I learned that Major General Walton H. Walker, a Cavalry and Armor officer of World War II fame as XXth Armored Corps Commander in General Patton's Third army, had a Military Police platoon as his guard, which he intended to convert to Armored Cavalry. I applied for, and was accepted into this unit, the 502nd Armored Cavalry Reconnaissance Platoon, for training as a machine gunner in a tank, and duty as a guard of the Commanding General and Headquarters, 8th U.S. Army. This was my favorite of all the units I served in, although most of my Army career was in Military Police work.

In June 1950, the North Koreans, under Russian direction, attacked the southern part of Korea, and the 8th Army was committed to a United States and United Nations effort to defend the free part of the Republic of Korea."

IN THE FIELD

MY M-24 TANK

"Our unit sailed from Japan to Korea on the first week of July. Our mission was to free all of Korea and to promote democracy for all Korean citizens. Unfortunately, in early September of 1951, our troops had to withdraw - we were losing the battle. They were tough times for our troops. Our troops were constantly on the move. We lost Seoul and recovered it twice. By Thanksgiving we had invaded North Korea and were in Pyongyang for dinner. Then the Chinese entered the war. We were outnumbered and had to withdraw. The conflict became a stalemate.

Our military leadership changed in Korea, and so did our mission as both Armored Cavalry and guards of the Commanding General and the Headquarters. We had been retained in that status by General Ridgway, but General Van Fleet who replaced him, did not want an elite unit as personal guards. He dismissed us from being personal guards and replaced us with a Military Police Company. He left our unit as Armored Cavalry; however, it was led by a Military Police Officer. Our mission remained as guards of the Headquarters only. Our platoon became part of a Military Police Company.

My twenty-one years in the United States Army were great times for me. These years gave me the training to develop my career as a Military Police Investigator and a Criminal Investigative Division (CID) Agent."

"You certainly have had a very interesting life, Mr. Opferman and you reached your goals." "Ellie and Joseph, I never want to stop learning. And, I will always take a strong interest in reading. Both of my parents graduated from Carnegie Institute of Technology in Pittsburgh, Pennsylvania. Myself, and all of my siblings were encouraged by our family to try our best and to make a positive difference in the lives of others." "Thank you for teaching Ellie and I so much, Mr. Opferman. How can Ellie and I help you with your program today?" "So, we have folded the programs for today's movie, and we can go inside and get the popcorn ready...the residents will soon be arriving."

"We would like to come back to help you again sometime, Mr. Opferman. Would that be okay?" "Of course. I would be grateful for your help."

CHRISTMAS DAY

"Emma, this Christmas dinner is delicious!" "Thank you, Clayton. I am grateful that we are here together sharing this meal, and grateful to have you with us for a few weeks."

"I have been counting the days until now - we have a lot to catch up on. Even though my Ellie and my Joseph have sent me so many wonderful photos and messages, I want to learn even more from them about their academics and their social activities."

"Joseph and I are so happy you are here, dad." Ellie, I know that this year we have all been brave and courageous, and we have worked together. I am thankful to your Gramms, Pops, and especially to you and your brother for being patient with me. Before you know it, the three of us will be having Gramms and Pops to our home for a dinner celebration. But for now, Emma and John, I am hoping that after we share our special meal together, we can open up some of the treasures that I have carried half way around the world for my family...and that includes our Liberty and our Valor." "Indeed, we can, Clayton. Joseph, would you grace our table with a prayer of thanks for this meal that we are sharing?" "Yes Pops, I will."

"Hi Ms. Baldwin." "Hello Ellie, good to have you back. I heard from your grandfather that the holidays were extra special for you and your brother Joseph." "Yes, our family was together and we had a great time. Joseph and I explained to our father about the volunteering that we have been doing at The Armed Forces Retirement Home, and about all that we have been learning from the people that we have come to know. He was glad to hear all of what we had to say, and when my dad returns in May, he will join us for some volunteering of his own. Hope that is okay with you, Ms. Baldwin."

"Of course, Ellie! I am looking forward to meeting your father. So, for today Ellie, there is a resident who would need some help organizing some personal historical documents that he has collected through the years. His name is Martin Francis Cody III. Mr. Cody was a Seaman First Class in the United States Navy. And, he has led quite a fascinating life. Mr. Cody joined the U.S. Navy at the age of twenty-one. He served during the Korean War. While serving our country, Mr. Cody was also the captain of the swimming and water polo teams - being an accomplished athlete was another part of Mr. Cody's service to his country. However, things changed when Mr. Cody was injured while working on an aircraft carrier. He was then medically retired from the U.S. Navy. School became a big part of his life. After earning multiple college degrees, Mr. Cody obtained jobs that took him to faraway places to work on fascinating projects. I believe Ellie, you will enjoy being of assistance to Mr. Cody, and you will have some very interesting history lessons during your volunteering hours with him. That's Mr. Cody sitting at the table - he is waiting for us."

"Ellie, I would very much like for you to meet Mr. Martin Cody."

"Hello Ellie, good to meet with you today." "Thank you, Mr. Cody. Ms. Baldwin has been kind to tell me about your career in the United States Navy, and some things about jobs that you have had through your life." "Ms. Baldwin knows a lot about the residents here at The Armed Forces Retirement Home. We are grateful for her expertise."

"Speaking of our library, I have work to do. If you need my help with anything, I will be close by." "Thank you, Ms. Baldwin. I have a few hours to volunteer today."

"Ellie, do you like to study history?" "Yes, I do Mr. Cody. I am definitely learning so much history and social studies here at The Armed Forces Retirement Home. How can I help you, this afternoon?"

"Recently, I have been reorganizing some of my personal and professional files. There is one particular collection that I could use some help with - it is some paperwork that tells the story of Liberty Island in New York Harbor. The reason that I have information about Liberty Island is because my grandfather Martin Cody I lived there for years. When my grandfather lived there, it was called by another name - Bedloe's Island." "What did your grandfather do while living on Bedloe's Island?" "Good question, Ellie. My grandfather and his brother came to New York from Ireland, when they were very young children. My grandfather was seven years old when his brother died...he was then alone."

"One day, my grandfather took a rowboat to Bedloe's Island and volunteered to work for his keep. He stayed on the island for years. Martin Cody I, married a school teacher and had eight children."

"My grandfather was the Assistant Lighthouse Keeper on Bedloe's Island. He learned so much while working there, and he had a good life. So, for years, I have collected and researched about Liberty Island. Ellie, would you be interested in helping me to put this paperwork in some kind of chronological order?"

"Mr. Cody, I can certainly try. If we don't finish today, maybe I could bring my brother Joseph with me another time and we could work on the project all together." "Good idea, Ellie. Let me show you a timeline of Liberty Island that I wrote. We can use this timeline as a guide to put the collection of my documents in order."

"Liberty Island is one of a group of islands in New York Harbor near the mouth of the Hudson River. Over Liberty Island have flown the flags of Holland, England, and the United States. For a brief time, Liberty Island was on loan to the French Government. It has also belonged to New York City, to the State of New York, and to several private owners. Long known as Bedloe's Island, it was renamed by an act of the United States Congress in 1956. Liberty Island is owned by our Federal Government and operated by the National Park Service. Since September 11, 2001, the island is guarded around-the-clock by patrols of the United States Park Police, Marine Patrol Unit. The Statue of Liberty, and Ellis Island are all part of the Statue of Liberty National Monument, listed on the National Register of historic places."

"So here are some interesting facts about Liberty Island that can help us put my collection of documents in order."

Liberty Island

"Great Oyster Island - In the mid-17th century, the Lenape native people lived on the island. It consisted of large tidal flats which were home to a vast number of oyster beds, a major source of food for the Lenape's. The Dutch settlers of New Netherland, the first European Colony in the Mid-Atlantic States named the land, Great Oyster Island."

"Bedloe's Island - In 1664, the Dutch surrendered Fort Amsterdam (a fort they had built) to the British. The English governor, Richard Nicolls granted the island to Captain Robert Needham. It was sold to Isaac Bedloe on December 23, 1667. The island remained in Mr. Bedloe's estate until 1732. In 1732, it was sold for five shillings to New York merchants - Adolphe and Henry Lane. While the two merchants owned the island, the city of New York temporarily established a smallpox quarantine station on the land."

** Lighthouse Construction - In 1746, Archibald Kennedy purchased the island for his summer residence, and built a lighthouse.

** Bedloe Island For Rent - In 1753, Archibald Kennedy advertised Bedloe Island for rent.

** Bedloe Island/Quarantine Station - In 1756, Archibald Kennedy allowed the island to be used as a smallpox quarantine station.

** Bedloe Island Sold - On February 18, 1758, the Corporation of the City of New York bought Bedloe Island.

** British Troops Occupy Bedloe Island - In 1776, British troops occupied New York Harbor, ahead of and up to the American Revolutionary War. The island was to be used for the housing of Tory refugees, American colonists who remained loyal to the British Crown. On April 2, 1776, the buildings constructed on the island for their own use were burned to the ground.

** Fort Wood - In 1811, the construction of a defensive fort built in the shape of an 11-point star was complete. Following the War of 1812, the star-shaped fort was named Fort Wood after Lieutenant Colonel Eleazer Derby Wood who was killed in the Siege of Fort Erie in 1813.

** Statue of Liberty - The statue, entitled "Liberty Enlightening the World," was a gift from the people of France in honor to the United States Centennial of Independence, and the friendship between France and the United States. In 1870, the French sculptor Auguste Bartholdi began designing the statue. Bartholdi visited the United States in 1871 to pick out a location for the historic gift - he chose Bedloe's Island. Auguste Bartholdi viewed Bedloe's Island as the "Gateway to America." The construction of the statue was completed in France in July 1884. The cornerstone was laid on August 5, 1884, and the pedestal of "Liberty Enlightening the World" was finished on April 22, 1886. The statue actually arrived in New York on June 17, 1885 on board a small French combat ship. The crates holding the statue were stored for eleven months while awaiting for its pedestal to be finished. It then took four months to reassemble "Liberty Enlightening the World." On October 28, 1886, the Statue of Liberty was unveiled by President Grover Cleveland. In 1956, Congress made official the name, Liberty Island.

"Mr. Cody, this is so amazing! I have learned so much history about Liberty Island today. If you don't mind, I would like to come back another time and help you to organize "all" of your historical documents." "Any time, Ellie. Take a copy of the timeline of Liberty Island with you...perhaps it might help you with some of your very own school studies. And, your brother Joseph could use the timeline as well." "Thank you, Mr. Cody. I had better get going-my grandfather is here to take me home." "Thank you, Ellie. And, thanks for all of your help today."

...

"So tell me Elanore, how was your visit with Martin Cody III?" "Pops, Mr. Cody is a remarkable and very interesting person. My volunteering with Mr. Cody today taught me so much about Liberty Island - I can't wait for dad to take Joe and me there for a visit." Mr. Cody gave me some information to take home, so that I can learn more about the history of the Statue of Liberty." "Indeed, Liberty Island is like no other place. And, how wonderful that Mr. Cody has shared so much personal history about such an important part of our nation's history. We should be on our way, Ellie. It's getting close to dinner time." "Thanks for volunteering today, Ellie." "You are welcome, Ms. Baldwin. I promised Mr. Cody that I would return sometime and continue to help him with some of his projects." "Mr. Cody would appreciate that very much, Ellie. I hope to see you soon." "Oh, for sure, Ms. Baldwin!"

DINNER TIME

"I have really worked up an appetite from baseball practice today. Gramms, this dinner tastes so good!" "I'm glad that you like it, Joseph." "Tell me Joseph, any new members on your baseball team?" "We have a few new players, and many of the same players that were on my team for Fall Ball. We have the same coaches - they are the best." "We are all looking forward to watching your games." "Thanks, Pops."

"Pops and Gramms, Ms. Baldwin would like me to volunteer and help a few more residents at The Armed Forces Retirement Home before I complete my Community Service Project report. My services hours with the residents of the Home have been so remarkable." "We are grateful Ellie, that your time spent there has been rewarding. Even though the school year will be coming to a close in the next few months, you can continue to volunteer at The Armed Forces Retirement Home." "You are so right, Gramms." "You know Ellie, I think I would like to accompany you for your next visit to the Home." "You are reading my mind, Joseph. I am glad that you will be joining me."

"Welcome. How great it is that both of you are here at the Home volunteering today. We have a resident that has a very special and unique story to tell - his name is George Johnson. He was a Chief Radioman (RMC) in the United States Navy. Mr. Johnson has invited you to visit with him and I will be joining you. He has some fascinating history to share with us. We'll be walking to the Sheridan Building where he lives...let's be on our way." "I have never met a Radioman, Ms. Baldwin." "I believe that you will learn a lot this afternoon, Joseph."

"Mr. Johnson, I would very much like you to meet Elanore and Joseph. They both have been volunteering here at The Armed Forces Retirement Home for some months." "Good to meet you Elanore and Joseph, and welcome to my home." "Thank you, Mr. Johnson. My sister Ellie and I have never met a Radioman. What exactly does that mean?" "Well Joseph, I was a Chief Radioman for the United States Navy. A Radioman is responsible for transmitting messages to people who are standing by and expecting to receive information. I began my duties as a Radioman using Morse code." "Mr. Johnson, I have heard of this. Morse code was mentioned in a book that I was reading not too long ago. Isn't it named after someone who was famous?" "That's correct, Joseph. Morse code is named for Samuel F.B. Morse, an inventor of the telegraph. Morse code is a method of transmitting text information as a series of on-off tones, lights or clicks that can be directly understood by a skilled listener or observer without special equipment. I actually have some information that I have saved on my computer. Let me print it for you and you can have it for keeps."

"Thanks so much, Mr. Johnson."

INTO THE SEAS

"I'm wondering if you traveled a lot for the United States Navy while you were serving our country?" "Indeed, I did, Elanore. I served on seven ships. One of the ships was an Icebreaker ship - the USS Atka. I also sailed on the USS Banner, an intelligence gathering ship that was the "sister" ship to the USS Pueblo. The USS Pueblo is a Banner - class environmental research ship. The Pueblo was attacked and captured by North Korean forces on January 23, 1968. This incident is known as the "Pueblo Crisis. The USS Pueblo remains in North Korea as a museum ship. I can surely tell the three of you that the United States of America was extremely upset about North Korea capturing the USS Pueblo. Pueblo is the only ship of the U.S. Navy still on the commissioned roster, currently being held captive by a foreign nation."

"Ellie and Joe, I have a book about the USS Pueblo in our library here at The Armed Forces Retirement Home. I can lend it to you and then perhaps you both could have another conversation with Mr. Johnson about this very topic." "That is a great idea, Ms. Baldwin."

"Mr. Johnson, how old were you when you joined the United States Navy?" "Good question, Elanore. At seventeen years of age, when I was a senior in high school, I was in the naval reserve."

Upon becoming eighteen years of age, it became possible for me to enlist in the Navy and become an active duty sailor. I had a fascinating career while serving our country. Here is something that I would like to show you. This is a photograph of myself receiving an award. The award was for Company Honor Man. I was the only Black man in my recruit training company." "Congratulations, Mr. Johnson." "Well, thank you Joseph."

RECEIVING AN AWARD

"Mr. Johnson, who inspired you the most while you were growing up?" "Good question, Elanore. I would say that my family did that for me. I was surrounded by good work ethics from childhood. My family took pride in work and completing whatever they started. My grandmother would say, "The servant is worthy of his hire." (1 Timothy 5:18).

"I lived with my grandparents in Frankfort, Ohio on a farm. Every day, we met the needs of the land and the animals on the farm. There's something else that I would very much like to show the three of you. This is a copy of my great-grandmother's Freedom Document. In 1806, the Commonwealth of Virginia passed a law that anyone who was freed after May 1st, 1806 had one year to leave Virginia in order to remain free, or they would be re-enslaved. My great-grandparents moved to Jackson County, Ohio and became farmers and landowners. And, I am certain that you haven't seen something like this. This document, dated August 29, 1864, is a copy of my great-grandfather's volunteer enlistment to serve as a soldier in The Civil War. My great-grandfather, Thomas E. Johnson, born in Halifax, Virginia, was a farmer and thirty-one years of age when he enlisted. My father served in the military in World War I as well. I have had some plenty remarkable role models throughout my entire life. When I retired from the United States Navy, I went to work as a civilian for the Navy. Working at March Air Force Reserve Base in California as an Instructor General, was another interesting part of my career."

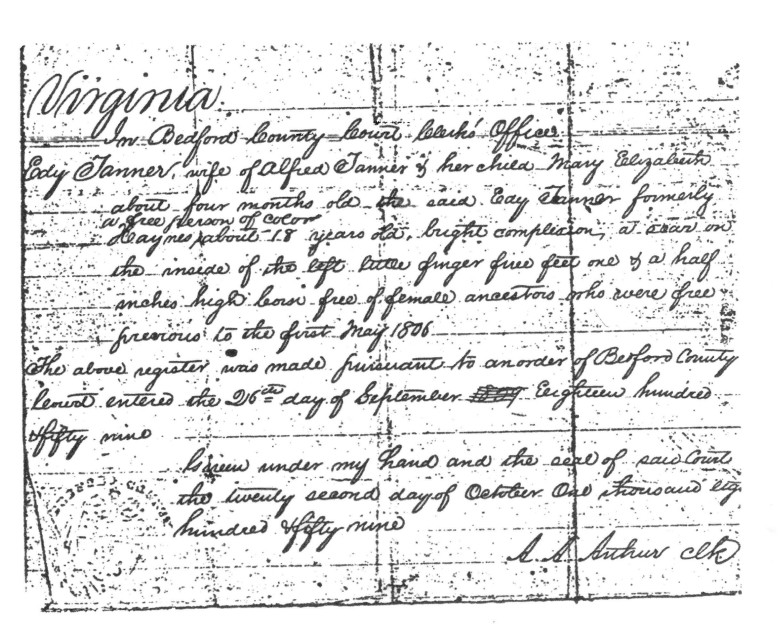

Virginia.

In Bedford County Court Clerks Office

Edy Tanner, wife of Alfred Tanner & her child Mary Elizabeth about four months old the said Edy Tanner formerly a free person of color

Haynes about 18 years old, bright complexion, a scar on the inside of the left little finger five feet one & a half inches high born free of female ancestors who were free previous to the first May 1806

The above register was made pursuant to an order of Bedford County Court entered the 26th day of September Eighteen hundred & fifty nine

Given under my hand and the seal of said Court the twenty second day of October One thousand eight hundred & fifty nine

A. L. Arthur Clk

71

VOLUNTEER ENLISTMENT.

STATE OF *Ohio*   **TOWN OF** *Chillicothe*

I, *Thomas E. Johnson*, born in *Halifax Co*
in the State of *North Carolina*, aged **31** years,
and by occupation a *Farmer*, DO HEREBY ACKNOWLEDGE to have
volunteered this *29* day of *August*, 1864,
to serve as a **Soldier** in the Army of the United States of America, for
the period of ~~THREE~~ *ONE* **YEARS**, unless sooner discharged by proper authority:
Do also agree to accept such bounty, pay, rations, and clothing, as are, or may be,
established by law for volunteers. And I, *Thomas E. Johnson*, do
solemnly swear, that I will bear true faith and allegiance to the **United States
of America,** and that I will serve them honestly and faithfully against all
their enemies or opposers whomsoever; and that I will observe and obey the
orders of the President of the United States, and the orders of the officers
appointed over me, according to the Rules and Articles of War.

Sworn and subscribed to, at *Chillicothe O*   *Thomas E. Johnson*
this *29* day of *August*, 186*4*
BEFORE *Hezekiah Abbey J.P.*

I CERTIFY, ON HONOR, That I have carefully examined the above-named Volunteer, agreeably
to the General Regulations of the Army, and that, in my opinion, he is free from all bodily defects and
mental infirmity, which would in any way disqualify him from performing the duties of a soldier.

W. S. Jones
Surg of Post and Sur. P.V.
EXAMINING SURGEON.

I CERTIFY, ON HONOR, That I have minutely inspected the Volunteer *Thomas E. Johnson*
previously to his enlistment, and that he was entirely sober when enlisted; that, to the best of my
judgment and belief, he is of lawful age; and that, in accepting him as duly qualified to perform the
duties of an able-bodied soldier, I have strictly observed the Regulations which govern the recruiting
service. This soldier has *Blue Eyes, Black hair, Light* complexion, is *five*
feet *Nine* inches high.

John F. Wilson 2nd Lieut
188th Regiment of *Ohio* Volunteers,
RECRUITING OFFICER.

(A. G. O. No. 74 & 76.)

"Mr. Johnson, this has been a remarkable visit today. I'm sure I can speak for Ellie and Joe and comment on how much we have learned from you this afternoon." "Well thank you, Ms. Baldwin. I'll be looking forward to seeing Elanore and Joseph on campus here at The Armed Forces Retirement Home. We appreciate our volunteers."

...

"Ellie and Joseph, did you enjoy your visit with Mr. Johnson today?" "Yes, of course Ms. Baldwin. I am amazed at all of the historical information Mr. Johnson has saved to the desktop on his computer. There is so much more to learn from him." "So true, Joseph. I'm sure Mr. Johnson wouldn't mind both yourself and Ellie making arrangements to meet with him for another lesson in history."

"Thanks, Ms. Baldwin. Joe, we are supposed to meet Gramms out front near the flagpole today. We had better get going. See you soon, Ms. Baldwin."

...

"Dinner tastes great, Gramms. Thank you for making such a delicious meal." "You are most welcome. Tell me Ellie, how is your Community Service report coming along?" "I am making some progress with my writing. There is just so much to include in the report. Mine and Joseph's volunteering at The Armed Forces Retirement Home has been such an amazing experience. And even though the school year is coming to a close soon, I want to continue my volunteering at the Home. There is so much to learn from the residents. I actually have an idea for my next school year - ninth grade."

"What's your idea, Ellie?" "Well Joseph, I would like to organize a group of students to routinely volunteer at The Armed Forces Retirement Home. We could visit after school and weekends." "That's a very good idea, Elanore. I would be happy to help you write a plan to promote this project. And, little by little I'm certain that you and your classmates would accomplish so much from your volunteering at The Armed Forces Home." "Thank you, Pops. I would love your help. Dad will be coming home soon, and I am sure that he will help, too." "Elanore, your father is going to be so pleased with what you and Joseph have learned this year from your time spent volunteering. Your grandmother and I are equally proud of what you and Joe have accomplished in school this year."

"It is Joseph and I that are grateful. Both you and Gramms have taken such great care of us. Joseph and I are so happy that dad has agreed to live here at your house for a while, once he returns from being overseas." "So are we Ellie and Joseph. This house is plenty big for the five of us. Actually, for the seven of us - to include Liberty and Valor. So, who is ready for dessert? I have made everyone's favorite."

"Welcome, Elanore. Ms. Baldwin told me that you would be here today, and I have set aside some time to walk the grounds of our Home with you." "Nice to meet you Mr. Lawrence." "I see your grandfather has accompanied you today, Elanore." "Good to see you Frank. Is the Public Affairs Office keeping you busy?" "Definitely is. You know that I have been volunteering in the Public Affairs Office since 2013 upon my return to The Armed Forces Retirement Home. One of my favorite responsibilities for this office is to give walking tours of our campus. And today, your granddaughter and I are going to do just that. Will you be joining us, John?" No. I will be in the Visitors Center catching up on some reading. Ellie can meet me there." "Very good. It's a beautiful day - let's get started."

...

"Elanore, here we are at President Lincoln's Cottage. Abraham Lincoln spent one-fourth of his presidency on the grounds of The Armed Forces Retirement Home, and it is believed that Lincoln wrote the last draft of The Emancipation Proclamation at what he called his summer White House - the Lincoln Retreat. As you can see Elanore, this historic home has been restored and is a National Monument. It has been open to the general public since 2008, after an eight-year restoration project. President Lincoln's Cottage is open to the public for an admission fee.

Our Home here is one of America's oldest veteran's retirement homes. The Soldier's Home was established in 1851 as an "asylum for old and disabled veterans. And today, our beautiful campus is situated in the heart of our Nation's Capital, and there is something for everyone who resides here."

"Mr. Lawrence, your Home is something very special. What about some of the other older homes that we are passing?" "Good question, Elanore. These buildings are listed as national historic landmarks. They were used for different purposes throughout the years. They are quite beautiful. Now, here we are at another landmark on the grounds of our campus - the Flagpole." "My brother Joseph and I attended the Veteran's Day celebration right here at this very spot, Mr. Lawrence. We had such a good time that day." "I am so glad that you were able to be a part of the Veteran's Day celebration here at The Armed Forces Retirement Home. Let's head back to Lincoln's Cottage and we can sit a while in the gazebo." "Good idea, Mr. Lawrence."

"Mr. Lawrence, would you mind telling me something about your career in the military?" "I wouldn't mind a bit, Elanore. On June 8 of 1948, I enlisted in The United States Air Force. After my basic training at Lackland Air Force Base in Texas, and Technical Training School for Fabrication and Survival Equipment - Parachute Rigging at Chanute Air Force Base, Illinois, I flew to England. There, I was stationed at Royal Air Force Burtonwood for depot assistance, on aircraft, flying the Berlin Airlift." "What is the meaning of the Berlin Airlift, Mr. Lawrence?"

IN MY UNIFORM

"Elanore, the Berlin Airlift began on June 26, 1948 and lasted until September 30, 1949. This mission was organized to carry supplies to the people of West Berlin. After World War II, the country of Germany was occupied by The Soviet Union, France, Great Britan, and The United States. The Soviet Union blocked roads, water access, and the railways to the Western Sectors of Berlin."

"How was the mission accomplished, Mr. Lawrence?" "Aircrews from the United States Air Force, the British Royal Air Force, the French Air Force, the Royal Canadian Air Force, the Royal Australian Air Force, the Royal New Zealand Air Force, and the South African Air Force flew over 200,000 flights in one year, providing supplies to the West Berliners, up to 8,893 tons of necessities each day, such as fuel and food. By the spring of 1949, the Berlin Airlift was clearly succeeding. On May 12, 1949, the Soviet Union lifted the blockade of West Berlin." "Was the mission a success, Mr. Lawrence?" "Yes, very much so. This mission demonstrated to the world that what had happened during World War II was not acceptable. We had to move forward in the right way after all that had happened during World War II."

"Thank you for explaining the Berlin Airlift to me, Mr. Lawrence." "Elanore, during this very historical mission, Air Force 1st Lieutenant Gail Halvorsen did something so special for the children that he saw in West Berlin. While he was flying loads of food, clothing, medicine, and fuel into West Berlin during the Soviet blockade, 1st Lieutenant Halvorsen saw children and he decided to lift their spirits and drop candy to them. His "Operation Little Vittles" gathered 23 tons of donated chocolate, raisins, chewing gum, and other treats for the children. Myself and my fellow comrades made the little parachutes for 1st Lieutenant Halvorsen's candy drops from the airplanes and we too donated candy for this special mission."

"This is all so interesting, Mr. Lawrence. We have learned about World War II during this school year - there is so much to know about this time in history."

"Elanore, you have years to study and learn about the World War II era. When I was growing up, my father taught me something very important. He impressed upon me to focus on the most important thing in my life at that very particular time, and to learn and grow from it. My father was my best teacher in life. Our entire family loved one another very much and we always took care of each other - even when times were tough. I believe it's about time to head to the Visitor's Center and meet up with your grandfather." "Okay, Mr. Lawrence. Thank you so much for the tour of your Home today - I learned so much." "You are most welcome, Elanore. Hope to see you soon."

"It's so good to be home with my family. Emma, this dinner is delicious." "Thank you, Clayton. We are so happy to have you home." "Ellie and Joseph, I have heard that you have my day planned tomorrow." "Yes, we do, dad. Our family is spending Memorial Day at The Armed Forces Retirement Home. Ellie and I are going to introduce you to some of the residents that we have come to know this year." "I can't wait to meet the veterans, Joseph."

"Dad, we are also going to tour the Soldiers Home National Cemetery. It was visited by President Lincoln. The cemetery is noted for being the first national cemetery, established in 1861. There will be a wreath laying ceremony at General John A. Logan's gravesite - he founded and formalized Memorial Day in 1868." "I can't think of a better way to spend the day honoring and remembering the people who died while serving in our nation's Armed Forces. And, I will be spending this important day with my family - the ones I love so very much."

BARBARA BRENNEN

BARBARA BRENNAN DANNAHER
"A WWII CODE GIRL"
"There will Always be a Story!"

Barbara Brennan, a resident of The Armed Forces Retirement Home, Washington, D.C. was born in Boston, Massachusetts, Dorchester Section, on November 23, 1920. When Barbara was four years of age, her parents moved to East Braintree, Massachusetts. Being that Barbara was an only child, her mother and her father wanted to bring their daughter up in a rural area of Massachusetts.

Upon graduating from Sacred Heart High School in East Braintree, Massachusetts, Barbara's father was transferred to Manchester, Connecticut for his job. While living with her parents in Manchester, Barbara began working as a bookkeeper for an automobile distributor. She enjoyed her work, and had become an active member of the community where she and her parents resided. Barbara was devoted to her church community, and she joined a "young adult group" that her pastor had orchestrated. It was during those times that Barbara met Thomas Dannaher-the two had their first date on December 7, 1941. That very same day in history, December 7, 1941, would change the world forever... The United States Naval Base at Pearl Harbor, the lagoon harbor on the island of Oahu, Hawaii, in the United States territory of Hawaii came under a surprise military strike conducted by the Imperial Japanese Navy. This attack came as a profound surprise to the American people and led directly to the American entry into World War II in both the Pacific and in Europe. Following the attack on Pearl Harbor, Thomas Dannaher joined the United States Marine Corps. In October, 1942, Barbara traveled to the Navy Enlistment Office, New York City, New York, to enlist for the Women Accepted for Voluntary Emergency Service, who came to be known as WAVES. Barbara Brennan was not quite twenty-one years of age; therefore, her parents signed for her to volunteer for the United States Navy.

She was "called up" for duty on December 12, 1942. Barbara traveled from Grand Central Station, New York City, to Cedar Falls, Iowa. During the next six weeks of Barbara's life, she and 1,050 girls experienced Basic Training. For much of the six weeks, the young women were assessed and completed some very rigorous testing. Then, from Cedar Falls, Iowa the WAVES were assigned to duty. Barbara Brennan then traveled to Washington, D.C. to live and work for the U.S. Navy at the Mount Vernon Seminary. The Navy acquired possession of Mount Vernon Seminary, a beautiful, private, and prestigious women's junior college located in northwest Washington on December 15, 1942. This educational institution that was built to shield its girls from the public, was to be a perfect place for shielding code breakers.

Cryptographers, also referred to as Code Breakers are individuals with strong backgrounds in mathematics, language skills, and they are extremely loyal individuals with a keen sense of integrity. During World War II, code breaking would come into its own as one of the most important forms of intelligence that exists. The code breakers of WWII advanced what is known as signals intelligence; reading the coded transmissions of enemies, and sometimes of allies. These women, The Code Girls, played a key role in shortening the war.

Barbara Brennan lived and worked at Mount Vernon Seminary, Washington, D.C. until October, 1945. Barbara was a cryptographer, a code breaker, for the United States Navy-her work included decoding "JN-25"(a code system that the Japanese had created using numbers rather than characters). She and her colleagues respected one another very much for their dedication and service to our beloved country, The United States of America. The WAVES played a significant role in ending World War II; V-J Day, August 15, 1945, "Victory in Japan."

Thomas Dannaher and Barbara Brennan were married on May 3, 1947. They raised six children together. Barbara's passion for children's literature led her to earn both a Bachelor of Science Degree in Library Studies, and a Master's Degree in Library Science.

Barbara Brennan

"PASS IN REVIEW!"

Largest Wave Quarters
MASSACHUSETTS AND NEBRASKA AVENUES

WAVE QUARTERS "D" . . . OUR HOME FOR TODAY

TO CREATE a home away from home is a task for energetic spirits and understanding minds. Young women from forty-eight states have succeeded in converting WAVE Quarters "D", Washington, D. C., from cold, gray barracks into a warm community which offers recreation for the leisure-minded, and opportunity for personal development in education and the art of living. From this home, Yeomen, Specialists, Electricians, Pharmacists, and Aerographers of the Women's Reserve go daily to important jobs . . . vital in bringing final victory to American shores. Since we are all an integrated group in the United States Navy, we achieve growth by working under Navy rules.

"D" calls many pictures to mind . . . The snappy marching by the company at drill, the shipshape barracks with comfort and friendliness, the aroma of newly-baked pastry from the mess hall, the fresh country tang to the rain-cleansed air, the change of watches at the front gate . . . and the dignity of "Colors" serenely enfolding this busy life in Navy blue.

Though often our hearts are far away as our hands are occupied in work or recreation, we always can find a solidarity of purpose and enjoyment in the active atmosphere of "D". This is our world for today! Here . . . we are the many states and nationalities of America fused into one.

When the time comes for us to resume our individual paths, we shall carry with us the warm memory of friendly sights and associations at "D" with the women who volunteered to serve . . . the WAVES of America.

JULY 1945

THE CODE BREAKERS

WITH MY FRIEND

Certificate of Satisfactory Service

UNITED STATES NAVY

NAVY DEPARTMENT · UNITED STATES OF AMERICA

THIS IS TO CERTIFY THAT

731 99 87   Mary Barbara BRENNAN
Specialist (Q) First Class (CR) (T)

*Has served and satisfactorily completed a period
of training and service on active duty in the
United States Navy, World War II*

SIGNATURE

NAVPERS 554

PERIOD OF ACTIVE DUTY	RIGHT INDEX FINGERPRINT
FROM	
15 December 1942	
TO	
31 October 1945	
TYPE OF SEPARATION	
Discharged	
CERTIFICATE NUMBER	
184666	
SIGNATURE	
Mary Barbara Brennan	

IF FOUND, DROP IN MAIL BOX, POSTMASTER: POSTAGE GUARANTEED.
RETURN TO: CHIEF OF NAVAL PERSONNEL, WASHINGTON 25, D.C.

THE ARMED FORCES RETIREMENT HOME

The Armed Forces Retirement Home is one of America's oldest veterans' retirement homes. The Soldier's home was established in 1851 as an "asylum for old and disabled veterans." Four of the original buildings still stand and are listed as national historic landmarks. Two of the buildings, Quarters 1 and the Lincoln Retreat served as the summer White House for U.S. Presidents Chester Arthur, Rutherford B. Hayes, James Buchanan, and most notably, Abraham Lincoln. Lincoln lived at the Soldier's Home in what is now called Lincoln Cottage during our nation's most turbulent time, the Civil War. Lincoln spent one-fourth of his presidency at the Soldier's Home, and it is believed that Lincoln wrote the last draft of the Emancipation Proclamation there.

The establishment that came to be known as the Soldier's Home was originally built for financier, George W. Riggs starting in 1842. Architect John Skirving designed the house situated on a hilltop overlooking downtown Washington, D.C. In 1851, the estate was purchased by the Federal Government for the purpose of building a home for veteran soldiers.

In June of 1862, the Lincoln Family set up housekeeping at the Riggs home and remained in residence until early November, a total of nearly five months. The next year, 1863, President Lincoln returned for another period of about four and a half months. Lincoln's stay in 1864 was somewhat shorter, extending from early July until sometime after mid-October. Abraham Lincoln lived at the Soldier's Home for about thirteen out of his forty-nine months in office. And, for most of that period his wife Mary, and his youngest son, Tad were with him.

Many significant events took place during the three long summers that Abraham Lincoln, his wife Mary, and their son Tad spent at the Soldier's Home. The Commander in Chief, President Lincoln, lived the battles of the Civil War year after year and made difficult and challenging decisions. In November of 1863, after spending a long summer at the Soldier's Home, Lincoln was prepared to travel North to Gettysburg to assist in the dedication of a new military cemetery. The Gettysburg Address culminated from months of reflection on the purpose of the Civil War.

Since its beginning as an "asylum for old and disabled veterans," the Armed Forces Retirement Home has been a residence for America's Finest. In 1991, Congress incorporated the U.S. Naval Home (opened in 1834) and the U.S. Soldier's and Airmen's Home (founded in 1851) into an independent establishment of the Executive Branch of the Federal Government, named the Armed Forces Retirement Home (AFRH) Agency. In 2002, the names of the two homes were officially changed to The Armed Forces Retirement Home-Gulfport and The Armed Forces Retirement Home-Washington. Military veterans from all branches of service can live at either Home.

Meet the storytellers. The nine women and men that shared a part of their lives-both personal and professional in their book, "Remembering With The Heart, Stories by America's Finest are truly remarkable individuals. They reside at The Armed Forces Retirement Home, Washington, D.C.

** **Edward Davis** enlisted in The United States Army in 1940 at the age of seventeen. His first duty station was Pearl Harbor where he was serving during the attack on Pearl Harbor, the lagoon harbor on the island of Oahu, Hawaii, in the United States Territory of Hawaii, on December 7, 1941. Edward Davis went on to serve in the Korean War, and the Vietnam War. Sadly, Ed Davis passed on January 29, 2018. He is deeply missed by his compatriots at The Armed Forces Retirement Home.

** **Catherine Deitch** served in the WAAC (Women's Army Auxiliary Corps) from December 30, 1942 to August 9, 1943. She then served in the WAC (Women's Army Corps) from August 9, 1943 to November 24, 1945. Catherine Deitch was an Administrative Specialist as the WAC Detachment First Sergeant at Headquarters Army Air Forces India, Burma Theater, Calcutta, India.

** **Robert M. Webb** joined The United States Army in 1944. His first assignment was in Le Havre, France at eighteen years of age. Robert M. Webb then moved on to Garmisch, Germany where he attended Military Ski School for two weeks. His "toughest" assignment was standing guard to the Nazi War Criminals in Nuremberg, Germany. Robert also worked in SS Trooper Prison Camps along with a Polish Military Company. Four of Robert M. Webb's brothers also served during WWII. Two of his brothers joined the United States Army Air Corps, one of his brothers joined the United States Navy, and the fourth brother joined the United States Marine Corps. Every branch of the service was represented by The Webb Family.

** **Norma Gene Strawn Rambow** joined the United States Marine Corps Women's Reserve on November 15, 1943. She attended Cooks and Baker's School, at Camp Lejeune, North Carolina, and she was assigned to Mess Hall 54 Battalion Area at Camp Lejeune. She served as an Assistant Cook, a Chief Cook, a Wing Sergeant (supervising the Mess Girls) and later a Supply Sergeant.

** **William J. Opferman** joined The United States Army in 1948, and was trained to be a radio operator. In Yokohama, Japan he was assigned to the radio company of the 304th Signal Battalion, the communication arm of the Eighth Army Headquarters. William J. Opferman's favorite assignment during his military career was with the 502nd Armored Cavalry Reconnaissance Platoon, Headquarters, Eighth, United States Army, in occupied Japan during the Korean War.

** **Martin Francis Cody** enlisted in The United States Navy at the age of twenty-one. He was Captain of the U.S. Navy Swimming and Water Polo Teams during the Korean War and the recipient of the U.S. Navy Jasper Award.

** **George Johnson** served in the United States Navy during the Korean War. He was a Chief Radioman that served on seven ships, including the USS Atka and the USS Banner - sister ship to the USS Pueblo.

** **Frank Lawrence** enlisted in The United States Air Force, on June 8 of 1948. He served in the Air Force from 1948 to 1968. In June of 1948, Frank Lawrence was aboard a plane that was part of a military operation called "The Berlin Airlift." He worked on aircraft at Tempelhof Airport in West Berlin, Germany. These planes brought supplies into Tempelhof to circumvent The Soviet Union's blockade of the Western Sectors of Berlin. Planes landed every 63 seconds. Frank Lawrence achieved the rank of Master Sergeant, E-8.

** Barbara Brennan Dannaher volunteered for the Women Accepted for Volunteer Emergency Service, who came to be known as WAVES. Barbara was called up for duty to serve for the United States Navy on December 12, 1942. She lived and worked at Mount Vernon Seminary, Washington, D.C. until October, 1945. Barbara was a cryptographer, a code breaker, for the United States Navy-her work included decoding "JN-25"(a code system that the Japanese had created using numbers rather than characters). The WAVES played a significant role in ending World War II; V-J Day, August 15, 1945, "Victory in Japan."

Letter to my Readers

This book speaks to what has been a part of my life throughout the years - volunteering. Even as a young child I can recall my parents, in particular my very own mother, encouraging me to raise my hand and get "out there" to make a difference in our community. I'm grateful for my mother's persistence and the "nudges" that she relentlessly gave to me during her life.

While writing *Remembering With The Heart - Stories by America's Finest*, I was reminded of the merit, the true value, and the generosity of spirit that a volunteer can bring to a given set of circumstances. The storytellers, nine veterans that reside at The Armed Forces Retirement Home, have spent their lives protecting our country and devoting themselves to family, friends, and communities far and wide. Upon numerous occasions, the residents of The Armed Forces Retirement Home and myself have spoken about the importance of volunteering and how it has played an integral part of both their personal and professional lives.

Remembering With The Heart – Stories by America's Finest, has been so much fun to orchestrate. The nine storytellers that I have come to know through the process of writing this book have become my friends. We read books together in our weekly book club meetings, we enjoy discussing current events, and we have fun sharing some delicious foods with one another.

The Armed Forces Retirement Home has been a special place in my heart since 1998. I first became acquainted with AFRH when asked to establish an intergenerational program for America's Promise - The Alliance for Youth. From that time on, I have remained a volunteer and a devoted fan to the residents of AFRH - *America's Finest*.

Glenna C. Orr

ACKNOWLEDGEMENTS

Writing "Remembering With The Heart, Stories by America's Finest," became one history lesson after the other, and for that I am most grateful. For years, it has been both an honor and a privilege to listen and learn from the veterans who reside at The Armed Forces Retirement Home, Washington, D.C.

Christine Baldwin, Librarian at The Armed Forces Retirement Home, is a very familiar face on the entire campus of AFRH. Not only does she orchestrate a beautiful library, Christine is a friend and strong supporter to those retiree's who have selflessly served our nation.

Christine Baldwin and myself began working together some five years ago. Initially, she and I collaborated with the "Creative Minds International Public Charter School" located in the historic Sherman Building on the grounds of The Armed Forces Home. Our goal was to put in place a "Reading Buddies" program with the veterans of AFRH and the students of this wonderful public charter school. Promoting literacy across the generations was such a fun and fulfilling initiative for both the young and the young at heart.

Being avid readers, Christine Baldwin and myself decided to have a go at developing a "Book Club" that would meet one afternoon a week to read and discuss literature selected by the members of our book club, the veterans that reside at AFRH. The rest remains history. Our "every Wednesday" literary discussions are lively, enlightening, and often times resembles a classroom of learning.

A heartfelt thank you to Harry F. Miller, SMSgt USAF(Ret) U.S. Army 740th Tank Battalion, Battle of the Bulge, Rhineland, and Central Europe; HQ Far East Command, Korean War, USAF, HQ Strategic Air Command, Vietnam. Mr. Miller resides at The Armed Forces Retirement Home, and he genuinely endorsed "Remembering With The Heart, Stories by America's Finest."

And, as has been for years, my gratitude goes to the men and women that have, and are presently serving in the United States Armed Forces. It is to them that this book is dedicated.

Most grateful,
Glenna C. Orr

Memories of My Own Family and My Friends

Photographs and Illustrations

Memories of My Own Family And My Friends

Reader's Notes

Font Selection:
Caslon - This is such a versatile font that it can be found in a wide variety of places. Benjamin Franklin used it extensively and in fact it was the font used to set both the Declaration of Independence and the U.S. Constitution. George Bernard Shaw required that all his plays be set in Caslon. In more modern times, it was the True Type Caslon Antique font that was used as the title font for the play Les Misérables.